Spot the Difference

Around the World

by Genie Espinosa

ARCTURUS

This edition published in 2019 by Arcturus Publishing Limited
26/27 Bickels Yard, 151–153 Bermondsey Street,
London SE1 3HA

Edited by Donna Gregory
Written by Lisa Regan
Illustrated by Genie Espinosa
Designed by Trudi Webb

ISBN: 978-1-78888-498-3
CH006741NT
Supplier 29, Date 0419, Print run 7913

Printed in China

Get a move on!

Turn the page to get started with your spot-the-difference adventure around the world!

There are **ten** differences to spot on each puzzle. Can you find them all?

What are you waiting for? Let's explore!

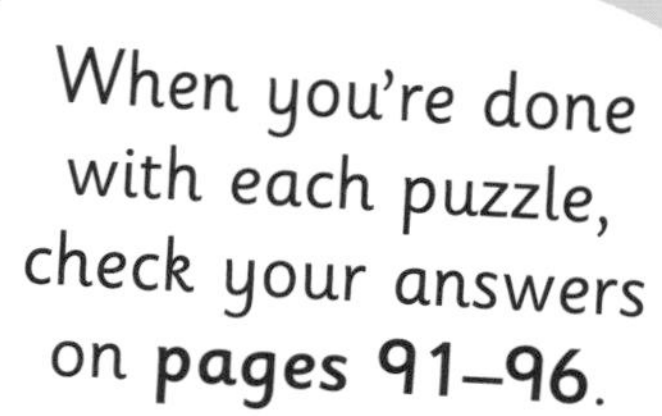

When you're done with each puzzle, check your answers on **pages 91–96**.

Can you find me on every page of the book?

READY TO GO!

Your flight has been called, so it's time to get on board. How exciting!

THE FROZEN NORTH

What's the best thing to do in Canada in the winter?
Get your skates on, of course!

CHOW DOWN!

Take time out in New York to grab a bite to eat!

THE GREAT OUTDOORS

Get back to nature on the Great Plains of North America.

BIENVENIDOS A MEXICO

Welcome to Mexico! It's fiesta time, so have fun trying to find the ten differences in this lively scene.

SLOW DOWN

Take it easy in Costa Rica, home to these adorable sloths.
Look for ten differences before you catch some zzzs.

HIGH IN THE HILLS

It's time for some hard work—a spot of farming in Peru.
Dig in!

THE BOTTOM OF THE WORLD

Not many people visit the Antarctic, but plenty of penguins call it home!

TRACK AND FIELD

Ready, set, go! South Africa is famous for sports—join the athletes on their big day. Don't forget to spot the differences.

FULLY LOADED

Set sail across the Indian Ocean from the coast of Tanzania.

NIGHT CREATURES

Lemurs and aye-ayes live only on the island of Madagascar.

ALL ABOARD!

There's no time to snooze on this Kenyan bus journey, but lots to look out for!

HUSTLE AND BUSTLE

It's always busy in the souks of Morocco.
Can you spot anything you like?

SKY HIGH

Dubai has some of the world's tallest, shiniest skyscrapers.

SUN WORSHIP

Head for the beach, and soak up some Turkish sun!

FEELING BLUE?

Don't be sad, blue is part of the national flag of Greece! Can you spot 10 differences in this charming seaside scene?

ON YOUR BIKE

The Italian lakes are beautiful, but cycling in those mountains can be tough! Stay on the level and spot ten differences.

CIAO, AMICO!

Tiptoe through the town square, so you don't disturb the birds! Is it a good time to taste the gelato?

ON REFLECTION

The Alhambra in Spain is a wonderful place of calm.

IN THE PINK

Join the flamingos on their annual migration route to Spain.

HOP ON BOARD

Taking a tram is a great way to get around Lisbon, Portugal's capital city. Keep looking for differences!

PARIS, FRANCE

Did you know that Canada, the USA, Panama, and Kiribati all have places called Paris? There's only one Paris, France, though.

TOUR DE FRANCE

These cyclists are racing past a field of jolly French sunflowers.

CANALSIDE

The Netherlands is famous for its canals, tulips, and bicycles.

TOWER BRIDGE

While you're visiting Europe, make sure you stop off in London. There are so many sights to see, but it's cool by the River Thames.

IN THE HIGHLANDS

Prepare to have your breath taken away by the Scottish scenery, and by the amazing wild deer!

FISHERMEN'S FRIENDS

Head over to the west coast of Ireland now, for a spot of fishing, and spotting the difference ...

TIME TO PLAY

This playground in Denmark is crazy and fun. Spot ten differences; they aren't easy to find!

COMING AND GOING

If you travel by train in Germany there's a high chance you will see Frankfurt Station. It is HUGE!

BACK TO NATURE

Relax and unwind for a while in the peace and quiet of Germany's Black Forest. Keep looking for differences, though!

FAIRYTALE CASTLE

A castle has stood at Bojnice in Slovakia for a thousand years.

SHADES OF OLD

Poland is famous for its brightly decorated buildings.

WATER BABIES

These lovely creatures feel right at home in the rivers of the Czech Republic. Join the fun by spotting ten differences!

MIDNIGHT SUN

The sun doesn't set in northern Finland during the summer.
It's a chance to have more fun outdoors!

CLIFFHANGER

The coasts of Iceland are the perfect home for puffins aplenty!
Millions of them gather here every spring.

ON THE SLOPES

Grab your skis and head to the Swedish mountains for some snowy spot the differences!

TAKE A HIKE

Enjoy the great outdoors in Norway, and walk past fjords and fields to really enjoy the country life!

RUSSIAN RIVER

The Moskva River runs past the majestic Kremlin in Moscow.

WILD HORSES

Many horses roam wild and free in Mongolia.

DIZZY HEIGHTS

The Himalayas are the tallest mountains in the world. Do you have enough of a head for heights to spot ten differences?

WATER WORLD

Parts of Hong Kong used to be under the ocean, but the land has been reclaimed. That's a real-life spot the difference!

BAMBOO BEAR

The forests of China are home to the iconic and adorable panda. Can you spot ten differences?

HIGH KICKS!

The sport of taekwondo comes from Korea.

LAND OF THE RISING SUN

Japan is just as astonishing when the sun goes down!

TINY TRANSPORT

Don't take a taxi in Thailand, take a tuk-tuk! It's a much faster way of zooming through the busy streets.

WELCOME, ALL!

The Lotus Temple in Delhi, India, is open to people of any religion, and looks like a beautiful flower.

FLY WITH ME

Kite flying is a popular pastime in Pakistan.
Lift your eyes to the skies to spot ten differences!

BENEATH THE SURFACE

There's plenty to see under the water on Australia's Great Barrier Reef. Spot ten differences as you snorkel.

HANGING AROUND

Let's do some spotting in Sydney, Australia!
Sydney Harbour Bridge is nicknamed the Coathanger.

ISLAND LIFE

More than 1,000 Polynesian islands are found in the Pacific Ocean. Some are volcanic hotspots. Spot ten differences!

WAR CRY

The haka is a traditional dance in New Zealand. Channel your inner warrior to solve this final spot-the-difference.

ANSWERS

4–5 READY TO GO!

6–7 THE FROZEN NORTH

8 CHOW DOWN!

9 THE GREAT OUTDOORS

10–11 BIENVENIDOS A MEXICO!

12–13 SLOW DOWN

14–15 HIGH IN THE HILLS

16–17 THE BOTTOM OF THE WORLD

18–19 SOUTH AFRICA

20 FULLY LOADED

21 NIGHT CREATURES

22–23 ALL ABOARD!

24–25 HUSTLE AND BUSTLE

26 SKY HIGH

27 SUN WORSHIP

28–29 FEELING BLUE?

30–31 ON YOUR BIKE

32–33 CIAO, AMICI!

34 ON REFLECTION

35 IN THE PINK

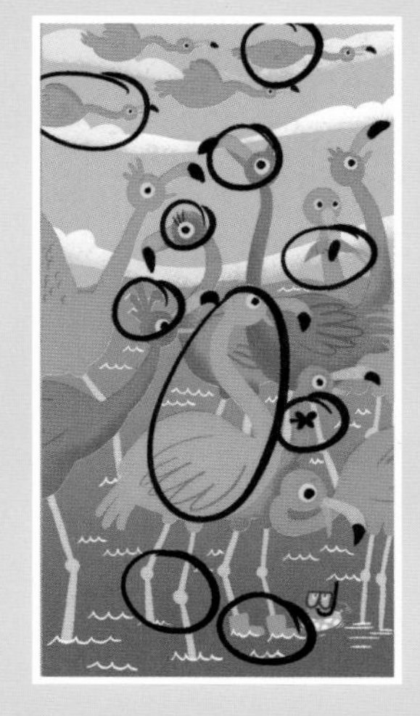

36-37 HOP ON BOARD

38-39 PARIS, FRANCE

40 TOUR DE FRANCE

41 CANALSIDE

42-43 TOWER BRIDGE

44-45 IN THE HIGHLANDS

46-47 FISHERMEN'S FRIENDS

48-49 PLAY TIME

50-51 COMING AND GOING

52-53 BACK TO NATURE

54 FAIRYTALE

55 SHADES OF OLD

56-57 WATER BABIES

58-59 MIDNIGHT SUN

60-61 CLIFFHANGER

62-63 ON THE SLOPES